THE FIRST MAN

Quran Stories for Little Hearts

by

S Khan

Goodwordkidz
Helping you build a family of faith

Long long ago, Allah was thought of making a beautiful world. So He created the beautiful universe, full of galaxies, planets, the moon, and stars all moving in harmony, all glorifying and praising Him.

2

4

When Allah decided to create a human
being, He collected every kind of soil and
mixed it like a potter's clay.

Moulding it into the shape of a man, Allah breathed His spirit into it. In this way, He gave life to the first man. The father of all of us. Allah named him Adam عليه السلام.

Today, people may all be of different colours, shapes and sizes, speaking different languages and living in different places. But they all have the same ancestor— the first man, Adam ﷺ. Allah made him the first prophet to guide people.

Allah bestowed many gifts upon Adam ﷷ. He gave him the gift of sight so that he might marvel at the creation of Allah, and the senses of hearing, smell, taste and touch to help him understand the universe around him.

9

Apart from all these blessings, Allah gave him the intelligence to be able to tell what was right and what was wrong and made him capable of doing good works. With this Allah gave him knowledge and wisdom and put him above the angels.

Allah also created the first woman, Hawwa (Eve) as a helper and loving companion of Adam علیه السلام. He told the couple to live in the garden of Paradise, but warned them not to approach a particular tree. Both of them began living there in perfect peace and happiness, with dazzling beauty all around them.

But Satan was jealous of them, seeing the honour they received from Allah. So one day, he came to Adam ﷺ and his wife and whispered to them, tempting them to approach the forbidden tree. He told them that it was the tree of eternal life, and that if they ate from it, they would never grow old, nor would they ever die.

14

Satan made them believe that he was giving them very friendly advice, so they ate from the tree and became wrongdoers. But no sooner had they done so, than they realized their fault and immediately turned towards Allah to say how sorry they were.

17

Allah forgave them both, but told them that since they had defied His orders, they would have to leave the gardens of Paradise and go down to earth. There Adam علیه السلام and Hawwa found themselves all alone, for no one else was living on the earth at that time.

Allah told them that from time to time His messengers and prophets would be coming to the earth to guide people to the true path.

20

Those who followed His directions and lived a good life would have no fear on the Judgement Day and would be admitted to Paradise. But those who disbelieved and rejected Allah's signs would be taken to task and thrown into the fire of Hell.

The story of the Prophet Adam عليه السلام teaches us that we have all been created by Allah, and that therefore, we are all equal. We should, then, respect each and every human being and never look down on others, or insult people. After all, we are all the children of one forefather— the Prophet Adam عليه السلام.

Find Out More

To know more about the message and meaning of Allah's words, look up the following parts of the Quran where the story of the Prophet Adam عليه السلام has been mentioned:

Surah Al Imran 2:30-38;
Surah al-Maidah 5:27-32;
Surah al-Araf 7:11-27;
Surah Ta Ha 20:115-23;
Surah Sad 38:71-85.

عليه السلام *Alayhis Salam* 'May peace be upon him.'
The customary blessings on the prophets.